Young people at work

A guide for employers

HSE BOOKS

This guidance is issued by the Health and Safety Executive.
Following the guidance is not compulsory and you are free to
take other action. But if you do follow the guidance you will
normally be doing enough to comply with the law. Health and
safety inspectors seek to secure compliance with the law and
may refer to this guidance as illustrating good practice.

C O N T E N T S

page III

This publication is a guide for employers on protecting the health and safety of young people at work

INTRODUCTION

1   This guide:

- describes general legislation for protecting the health and safety of young people at work;
- explains which risks apply particularly to young workers (those under 18 years old);
- tells you what you need to do to comply with the law; and
- tells you what specific legislation applies.

It also lists Approved Codes of Practice (ACOPs) and other guidance which you may find helpful in identifying and tackling specific risks to young people.

General duties for all employers

2   The law at present requires you to assess risks to all your employees, including young workers, and to do what is reasonably practicable to control those risks.

3   Young workers are seen as being particularly at risk because of their possible lack of awareness of existing or potential risks, immaturity and inexperience. Children under 13 years old are generally prohibited from any form of employment. Children between 13 and the minimum school leaving age (MSLA)* are prohibited from being employed in industrial undertakings such as factories, construction sites etc, except when on work experience schemes approved by the local education authority. The Health and Safety (Training for Employment) Regulations 1990 have the effect of designating children on work experience as employees for the purposes of health and safety legislation. Employers offering work experience placements to children must provide them with at least the same health, safety and welfare protection that they give their own employees. There are also some age-related restrictions which prohibit young workers, including children on work experience, from working with particular machinery or undertaking particular tasks. A list of these is at Appendix 1.

4   New legislation required to implement the health and safety provisions of the *European Directive on the protection of young people at work* came into force on 3 March 1997. This legislation, the Health and Safety (Young Persons) Regulations 1997,† introduces new requirements into the Management of Health and Safety at Work Regulations 1992** (the Management Regulations).

*   Just before or just after their 16th birthday
†   SI No 135/1997
** SI No 2051/1992, amended by SI No 2865/1994

5 As a result employers are required to:

- assess risks to young people, under 18 years old, *before* they start work;
- take into account their inexperience, lack of awareness of existing or potential risks, and immaturity;
- address specific factors in the risk assessment;
- provide information to parents of school-age children about the risk and the control measures introduced; and
- take account of the risk assessment in determining whether the young person should be prohibited from certain work activities, except where they are over MSLA and it is necessary for their training and:

  - where risks are reduced so far as is reasonably practicable; and
  - where proper supervision is provided by a competent person.

6 The requirements in paragraph 5 do not apply to occasional work or short-term working involving:

- domestic service in a private household;
- work regarded as not being harmful, damaging or dangerous to young people in a family undertaking.

In this context 'family undertaking' is thought to mean small and medium-sized firms owned by, and employing members of, the same family.*

* Husbands, wives, fathers, mothers, grandfathers, grandmothers, stepfathers, stepmothers, sons, daughters, grandsons, granddaughters, stepsons, stepdaughters, brothers, sisters, half-brothers and half-sisters.

7   However, like other employers, such firms must ensure they comply with other health and safety requirements such as carrying out a risk assessment. This will help them establish whether the work is harmful, damaging or dangerous to young people.

WHAT YOU NEED TO DO

Risk assessment

8   The Management Regulations require you to make a suitable and sufficient assessment of the risks to the health and safety of all your employees and identify groups of workers who might be particularly at risk. The associated Approved Code of Practice specifically identifies young or inexperienced workers as such a group. Your assessment of the risks to the health and safety of young workers must take into account their inexperience, lack of awareness of existing or potential risks, and immaturity.

9   You must also take into account the following factors:

- the fitting-out and layout of the workplace and the workstation;
- the nature, degree and duration of exposure to physical, biological and chemical agents;
- the form, range and use of work equipment and the way in which it is handled;
- the organisation of processes and activities;
- the extent of the health and safety training provided, or to be provided, to the young people concerned; and

● risks from agents, processes and work listed in the Annex to the Directive.

10 The extent of the risk will determine whether you should restrict the work of your young workers. Table 1 provides more information on the nature of the risks and what to do about them. It includes a list of agents, processes and work, taken from the Annex to the Directive, which are considered by the European Commission as likely to give rise to dangers to young people. If, despite following the advice in the table, you conclude as a result of your risk assessment that there is a significant risk to young people doing this type of work, you must prohibit them from doing it.

11 You must carry out the risk assessment *before* the young worker is employed. There is no need for you to carry out a further risk assessment as a result of the new Regulations, providing that your current one has taken account of the characteristics of your young workers and included consideration of the factors listed in paragraph 9. You may wish to consider developing generic risk assessments for employing young people. These might be especially useful when young people are likely to undertake transient work and could be modified to deal with particular work situations to ensure that young people are not exposed to unacceptable risks.

Information for parents

12 You are required by the Management Regulations to tell all your workers, including young workers, about the risks to their health and safety identified by the assessment and the measures put in place to control them.

13   You must also let parents of young workers under the MSLA know the key findings of the risk assessment and the control measures taken. There is no requirement to provide this information in writing and, in the case of work experience, there is scope for you to involve organisers such as schools, TECs, Lecs, Education Business Partnerships and other work experience agencies in getting information to parents or guardians of any child seeking a placement. HSE is working with the Department for Education and Employment on the development of health and safety guidance for organisers of work experience. This will explain your duties and how organisers might help you comply with them. You might also consider asking the child to pass on the information on your behalf, as long as you are confident this would be done.

14   For this information to serve any useful purpose you must ensure that parents or guardians are provided with it before employment or work experience starts. You may want to consider giving this information to trade union safety representatives, or representatives of employees' safety.

Restrictions on the work of young people

15   The outcome of your risk assessment and the extent of the control measures you introduce will determine whether significant risk or harm to the young worker remains. In most cases, if you are complying with existing health and safety legislation, for example the Manual Handling Operations Regulations 1992, or the Control of Substances Hazardous to Health Regulations 1994 (COSHH), the risks to young workers will be adequately controlled. You may wish to refer to the Approved

Codes of Practice and guidance listed at Appendix 2, or seek professional advice on identifying and controlling the risks.

16   If a significant risk remains despite your best efforts to do what is reasonably practicable to control harmful exposure to substances at work, or significant risks to young workers undertaking particular work, you must not employ young workers to do this work. The type of work, nature of the risk, and how to avoid it are described in Table 1 (pages 8 to 41). In these circumstances you may consider transferring the young worker to other work and replacing them with a more experienced adult. However, in doing so you will need to ensure that you are complying with other health and safety legislation. You will need to review the risk assessment if the nature of the work changes or if you suspect that it is no longer valid.

Training

17   The prohibitions will not apply where young people *over* MSLA are doing work necessary for their training, under proper supervision by a competent person, and providing risks are reduced so far as is reasonably practicable, in line with existing health and safety legislation. 'Training' includes Government-funded training schemes for school leavers, modern apprenticeships, in-house training arrangements and work qualifying for assessment for N/SVQs, eg craft skills. But the prohibitions will continue to apply to children under MSLA who are employed or undergoing training such as work experience.

Table 1: HAZARDS, RISKS, AND WAYS OF AVOIDING THEM

- You must *not* employ people in the work activity listed in the table (**IN BOLD CAPITALS**) if you identify significant risks to their
- Listed in the table are agents, processes and work taken from the Annex to the *European Directive on the protection of young people at w*

List of agents, processes and work	What is the risk?
WORK OBJECTIVELY BEYOND PHYSICAL OR PSYCHOLOGICAL CAPACITY	
Physical capacity	Accidents, injuries and/or musculoskeletal disorders which can occur in jobs that require repetitive or forceful movements, particularly in association with awkward postu or insufficient recovery time.
Work the pace of which is determined by machinery and which involves payment by results	Young workers may be more at risk as their muscle strength may not be fully developed, and they may be less skilled, eg in handling techniques or in pacing the work according to capacity. They may also be more subject to peer pressure to take on tasks that are too much for them or to work more quickly.

afety which cannot be avoided

3/EC), which the EC considers are likely to give rise to dangers to young people

How to avoid the risk	Other legislation
The risk assessments should take account of physique and general health, age and experience. Training and effective supervision should be provided.	Manual Handling Operations Regulations 1992
The risk assessments should take account of age and experience. Training and effective supervision should be provided.	

List of agents, processes and work	What is the risk?
WORK OBJECTIVELY BEYOND PHYSICAL OR PSYCHOLOGICAL CAPACITY *(continued)*	
Psychological capacity	Although there will be large individual differences in the psychological capacity of young people, based on difference in training, experience, skills, personality and attitudes, in the vast majority of jobs there is no difference in the kind of mental and social skills used by young people and adults. However, there are some areas of work that could be beyond a young person's mental and emotional coping ability, such as dealing with violent and aggressive behaviour and decision-making in stressful situations.

How to avoid the risk	Other legislation
The risk assessment should focus on critical tasks which rely on skill, experience and an understanding of the task requirements. Training and effective supervision should be provided, particularly where the young person might be using machinery with exposed dangerous parts, eg food slicing machinery.	

List of agents, processes and work	What is the risk?
WORK INVOLVING HARMFUL EXPOSURE TO AGENTS WHICH ARE TOXIC, CARCINOGEN ANY OTHER WAY CHRONICALLY AFFECT HUMAN HEALTH	
Physical agents *Work in high-pressure atmospheres*	*Compressed air*: People who work in compressed air are at ri of developing the bends. This is due to free bubbles of gas i the circulation caused by too rapid a return to atmospheric pressure during decompression. Young workers are not inherently more at risk, although immature behaviour may increase the risk of it occurring. Also, young workers have bones which are not fully developed and may be at greater risk of long-term harm from the bends.
	Diving: The risks are from pressure and decompression.

How to avoid the risk	Other legislation
USE HERITABLE GENETIC DAMAGE, OR HARM TO THE UNBORN CHILD, OR WHICH IN	
Strict compliance with HSE-approved decompression procedures. It is current industry practice not to allow people below the age of 18 to work in compressed air. This practice is supported by HSE. If work is necessary, HSE-approved decompression procedures should be followed.	Work in Compressed Air Regulations 1996
Divers must have an HSE certificate of competence, be fit and must have a valid certificate of medical fitness to dive. There is no minimum age limit for divers. However, it is unusual for anyone below school-leaving age to undergo diver training and no one under 18 is accepted for work by employers offshore.	Diving Operations at Work Regulations 1981 as amended by the Diving Operations at Work (Amendment) Regulations 1990 and the Diving Operations at Work (Amendment) Regulations 1992 (under review)

List of agents, processes and work	What is the risk?
WORK INVOLVING HARMFUL EXPOSURE TO AGENTS WHICH ARE TOXIC, CARCINOGE ANY OTHER WAY CHRONICALLY AFFECT HUMAN HEALTH *(continued)*	
Biological agents	Despite physical and physiological immaturity, young workers are not intrinsically more susceptible to infections from biological agents than adults. Like any other worker, they may be at greater risk if they suffer from any disease or from the effects of medication or pregnancy.
Chemical agents ★ *Very toxic, toxic, harmful, corrosive and irritant substances*	Young people are not physiologically at any greater risk from exposure to such substances than anyone else. The actual risk can only be determined following a risk assessment of the particular substance at the place of work. However, young people may not appreciate the dangers to their health or they may not understand or follow instructions properly because of their immaturity.

★ The list of chemical agents listed in the Annex to European Directive (94/33/EC) is not reproduced as there are some technical inconsistencies with ex Directives. However, the table should provide sufficient description to enable those substances in the scope of the Regulations to be identified.

How to avoid the risk	Other legislation
USE HERITABLE GENETIC DAMAGE, OR HARM TO THE UNBORN CHILD, OR WHICH IN	
Precautions against risk of infection at work and of acquiring an allergy to certain microbes are applicable to all employees regardless of their age or state of health. Control measures, which are often as simple as maintaining high standards of hygiene like hand-washing or use of gloves, are derived from the risk assessment that employers are required to make under the COSHH Regulations. Vaccination should be offered as a supplement to procedural or physical controls.	Control of Substances Hazardous to Health Regulations 1994 (COSHH) Genetically Modified Organisms (Contained Use) Regulations 1992 as amended by the Genetically Modified Organisms (Contained Use) (Amendment) Regulations 1996
These substances fall within the scope of COSHH. Employers should assess the health risks to young people, arising from work with any of the substances, and where appropriate prevent or control the risks. Particular attention should be paid to COSHH requirements on the provision of information, instruction and training, and to the provision of adequate supervision within a safe system of work.	Control of Substances Hazardous to Health Regulations 1994 (COSHH)

List of agents, processes and work	What is the risk?
WORK INVOLVING HARMFUL EXPOSURE TO AGENTS WHICH ARE TOXIC, CARCINOGE ANY OTHER WAY CHRONICALLY AFFECT HUMAN HEALTH *(continued)*	
Chemical agents *(continued)*	Some substances (*carcinogens*) may cause cancer. They nee special consideration because of that property - they have r special effect on young people.
	Some substances can cause *allergic reactions* in people. Thi may give them dermatitis or asthma. These substances do not affect young people any differently from adults.
	Some substances may impair people's ability to have children or may damage the unborn child. These substanc do not affect young people any differently from adults.

How to avoid the risk	Other legislation
SE HERITABLE GENETIC DAMAGE, OR HARM TO THE UNBORN CHILD, OR WHICH IN	
There are special precautions for these kinds of substance as set out in the COSHH Carcinogens ACOP. Many of these substances can be identified from the label or safety data sheet for the substance which will say 'May cause cancer'. Other carcinogenic substances and processes are listed in Schedule 8 of the COSHH Regulations (see the COSHH Carcinogens ACOP).	
HSE guidance on preventing asthma at work, and on dermatitis, gives practical advice on preventing risk to all workers.	

List of agents, processes and work	What is the risk?

**WORK INVOLVING HARMFUL EXPOSURE TO AGENTS WHICH ARE TOXIC, CARCINOGE
ANY OTHER WAY CHRONICALLY AFFECT HUMAN HEALTH** *(continued)*

Lead and lead compounds	Young people aged 16 and 17 are not physiologically at an greater risk from exposure to lead and its compounds than anyone else.

Lead and its inorganic compounds are known to produce diverse biological effects in humans, depending on the exposure level. These range from minor biochemical chang in the blood, which are unlikely to have adverse health consequences, to severe irreversible or life-threatening disruption of body processes, in particular the nervous system, the blood-forming system and the kidneys. There also concerns about the effects of lead on the quality of semen and on the unborn child. |

How to avoid the risk	Other legislation
SE HERITABLE GENETIC DAMAGE, OR HARM TO THE UNBORN CHILD, OR WHICH IN	
The employment of young people for work in certain lead processes is forbidden. For other processes, employers should ensure that they adequately control the exposure of young people to lead and its compounds, in accordance with the Control of Lead at Work Regulations 1980 and ACOP. Special attention should also be paid to the requirements on the provision of information, instruction and training, and to the provision of adequate supervision within a safe system of work.	The Factories Act 1961, sections 74, 128, 131 and 132; Paints and Colours Manufacture Regulations 1907; Yarn (Dyed by Lead Compounds) Heading Regulations 1907; Vitreous Enamelling Regulations 1908; Tinning of Metal Hollow-Ware, Iron Drums and Harness Furniture Regulations 1909; Lead Smelting and Manufacture Regulations 1911; Indiarubber Regulations 1922; Electric Accumulator Regulations 1925; Pottery (Health and Welfare) Special Regulations 1950 (all under review) Control of Lead at Work (CLAW) Regulations 1980 (under review) and ACOP (under review)

List of agents, processes and work	What is the risk?

WORK INVOLVING HARMFUL EXPOSURE TO AGENTS WHICH ARE TOXIC, CARCINOG
ANY OTHER WAY CHRONICALLY AFFECT HUMAN HEALTH *(continued)*

Lead and lead compounds *(continued)*	The toxic effects of lead alkyls are primarily neurological c psychiatric. Symptoms include agitation, insomnia, dizziness, tremors and delirium, which can progress to mania, coma and death. These symptoms are accompanie by nausea, vomiting and abdominal pain. The actual risk can only be determined following a risk assessment of the particular circumstances under which th is exposure to lead or its compounds at the place of work. However, young people may not appreciate the dangers to their health or they may not understand or follow instructions properly because of their immaturity.

How to avoid the risk	Other legislation
ISE HERITABLE GENETIC DAMAGE, OR HARM TO THE UNBORN CHILD, OR WHICH IN	

List of agents, processes and work	What is the risk?
WORK INVOLVING HARMFUL EXPOSURE TO AGENTS WHICH ARE TOXIC, CARCINOGEN ANY OTHER WAY CHRONICALLY AFFECT HUMAN HEALTH *(continued)*	
Asbestos	Young people are not physiologically at any greater risk fro exposure to asbestos than anyone else, but asbestos is a ve hazardous material.
	Exposure to asbestos fibres causes three serious diseases: mesothelioma (a cancer of the lung lining); lung cancer (indistinguishable from cancers caused by other agents); a asbestosis (scarring of the lung tissue). These diseases can take many years to appear after the period of exposure. There are no cures for asbestos-related diseases.
	The actual risk can only be determined following a risk assessment of the particular circumstances under which th is exposure to asbestos at the place of work. However, you people may not appreciate the dangers to their health or th may not understand or follow instructions properly becaus of their immaturity.

How to avoid the risk	Other legislation
JSE HERITABLE GENETIC DAMAGE, OR HARM TO THE UNBORN CHILD, OR WHICH IN	
The requirements of the Control of Asbestos at Work Regulations 1987 (CAW) should be followed. In particular, exposure to asbestos should be avoided wherever possible. If exposure cannot be avoided, for example by using other products or processes, it should be reduced to as low a level as is reasonably practicable. Special attention should be paid to CAW requirements on the provision of information, instruction and training, and to the provision of adequate supervision within a safe system of work.	Control of Asbestos at Work Regulations 1987 (CAW)
The marketing and use of certain asbestos materials and products is forbidden.	Asbestos (Prohibitions) Regulations 1992

List of agents, processes and work	What is the risk?
WORK INVOLVING HARMFUL EXPOSURE TO RADIATION	
Ionising radiations	The risk of developing cancer and hereditary defects from exposure to ionising radiation, which increases slightly for younger age groups, is controlled by setting statutory annual dose limits. The dose limits for young trainees are set at 30% of the adult limits.
Non-ionising electromagnetic radiation	*Optical radiation:* There is no evidence that young workers face greater risk of skin and eye damage than other workers.
	Electromagnetic fields and waves: Exposure within current recommendations is not known to cause ill health to workers of any age. Extreme overexposure to radio-frequency radiation could cause harm by raising body temperature.

How to avoid the risk	Other legislation
Work procedures should be designed to keep exposure to ionising radiation as low as reasonably practicable. Young people are not permitted to be designated as 'classified persons' and should only enter a 'controlled area' under the terms of a written system of work.	Ionising Radiations Regulations 1985 and supporting ACOP
Outdoor workers are advised to reduce their exposure to the sun in the summer months as much as is reasonably practicable and follow HSE guidance. Occupational exposures to visible and infra-red radiation should not exceed the maxima recommended by ACGIH.* The IRPA/INIRC (ICNIRP)† 1989 guidelines should be followed for ultraviolet (UV) exposures (see Appendix 2). BS EN 60825-1 tabulates maximum permissible exposure levels and light-emitting diode (LED) radiations according to wavelength and exposure time. Exposure to *electric and magnetic fields* should not exceed the restrictions on human exposure published by the National Radiological Protection Board.	None specific

---

* American Congress of Government Industrial Hygienists.

† International Commission on Non-Ionising Radiation Protection (ICNIRP) (developed in 1992 out of the International Non-Ionising Radiation Committee (INIRC) and a committee of International Radiation Protection Association (IRPA)).

List of agents, processes and work	What is the risk?
WORK INVOLVING THE RISK OF ACCIDENTS WHICH IT MAY BE ASSUMED CANNOT BE ATTENTION TO SAFETY OR LACK OF EXPERIENCE OR TRAINING	
Manufacture and handling of devices, fireworks or other objects containing explosives	Greater risk of fire or unintended initiation of explosives because of lack of experience, lack of awareness or mental immaturity on the part of young workers may lead to inadequate observance of safety precautions.

How to avoid the risk	Other legislation
ISED OR AVOIDED BY YOUNG WORKERS OWING TO THEIR INSUFFICIENT	
Young workers must not enter or be employed in a danger building or explosives store, except in the presence and under the supervision of a responsible adult. By law this person must be aged 21 or over. People under 16 must not normally be employed in explosives buildings.	Explosives Act 1875 (as amended by the Explosives Act 1923) and subsidiary legislation (currently under review)

List of agents, processes and work	What is the risk?

WORK INVOLVING THE RISK OF ACCIDENTS WHICH IT MAY BE ASSUMED CANNOT BE ATTENTION TO SAFETY OR LACK OF EXPERIENCE OR TRAINING *(continued)*

Work with fierce or poisonous animals	Some animals kept in zoos are fierce or poisonous. Farm animals may occasionally show aggression, eg bulls or animals with young. Young workers may be more at risk th older workers because of their inexperience and lack of appreciation of the risks.

How to avoid the risk	Other legislation

NISED OR AVOIDED BY YOUNG WORKERS OWING TO THEIR INSUFFICIENT

How to avoid the risk	Other legislation
All employees working with zoo animals must be supervised. Because of their lack of experience young workers may be particularly at risk and zoo operators should ensure they are adequately trained and strictly supervised. Safety management systems should also be put into place to segregate employees from potentially fierce animals. If you know that a farm animal is normally aggressive, consider disposing of it. Otherwise: • prevent access to potentially aggressive farm animals; • provide proper training for young workers before they have to work among male animals or those with young; • make sure adequate handling facilities are available and used; and • provide supervision until you are satisfied the young worker is competent.	Agriculture (Avoidance of Accidents to Children) Regulations 1958 (currently under review)

List of agents, processes and work	What is the risk?
WORK INVOLVING THE RISK OF ACCIDENTS WHICH IT MAY BE ASSUMED CANNOT BE [ATTENTION TO SAFETY OR LACK OF EXPERIENCE OR TRAINING *(continued)*	
Animal slaughtering on an industrial scale	Risks from mechanical equipment and the operation of stunning equipment, animal handling and zoonotic infectic
Work involving the handling of equipment for the production, storage or application of compressed, liquefied or dissolved gases *Flammable liquids*	Accidental spills can cause fires or explosions. Flammable liquids should be used only for their intended purposes; using them for other purposes may lead to fires or explosioɪ

How to avoid the risk	Other legislation
SED OR AVOIDED BY YOUNG WORKERS OWING TO THEIR INSUFFICIENT	
Young workers should be carefully instructed and supervised to follow recognised industry safe systems.	None specific
It may be necessary to explain the basics of flammability and what to do if liquid is spilt. It may also be necessary to point out the dangers of using liquids, such as petrol, for cleaning machinery or starting bonfires.	

List of agents, processes and work	What is the risk?
WORK INVOLVING THE RISK OF ACCIDENTS WHICH IT MAY BE ASSUMED CANNOT BE **ATTENTION TO SAFETY OR LACK OF EXPERIENCE OR TRAINING** *(continued)*	
Flammable gases	Leaking gas from pipes, appliances or cylinders can cause fires or explosions.
Gas cylinders	There is no evidence that young workers face greater physi risks from a release of stored energy than other workers. Leaking gas from cylinders may cause fires or explosions. Physical damage to cylinders may cause leaks which may le to fires or explosions. Heavy cylinders may cause physical injury if not properly handled. Application of heat to gas cylinders may cause them to bur possibly resulting in a 'shrapnel' type explosion. Alternatively, the contents may be vented through a pressu release valve resulting in fire or explosion.

How to avoid the risk	Other legislation
ISED OR AVOIDED BY YOUNG WORKERS OWING TO THEIR INSUFFICIENT	
It may be necessary to explain the basics of flammability; people need to know how to detect leaking gas and what to do in the event of a gas leak.	
It may be necessary to explain the basics of flammability; people need to know how to detect leaking gas and what to do in the event of a gas leak. Gas cylinders need to be properly handled, both to avoid the danger of fire or explosion, and the risk of physical injury to the worker, eg crushed toes. Gas cylinders need to be safely stored and used, away from direct sources of heat.	

List of agents, processes and work	What is the risk?
WORK INVOLVING THE RISK OF ACCIDENTS WHICH IT MAY BE ASSUMED CANNOT BE ATTENTION TO SAFETY OR LACK OF EXPERIENCE OR TRAINING *(continued)*	
Work with vats, tanks, reservoirs or carboys containing chemical agents	Such work involves handling or working near to substantial quantities of substances hazardous to health. There is a risk of fire or explosion where there is an explosive atmosphere, or where spills or leaks of flammable substances are readily foreseeable. There is also a risk of ignition of a flammable liquid which has splashed or soaked into clothing.

How to avoid the risk	Other legislation
ISED OR AVOIDED BY YOUNG WORKERS OWING TO THEIR INSUFFICIENT	

The risk assessment should consider issues such as: • how to ensure that young people will follow emergency procedures properly if containment is lost; • how to prevent young people from falling into tanks of hazardous chemicals; and • how to ensure that young people behave responsibly when working near quantities of chemicals that have the potential to cause serious harm, eg making young workers aware of the dangers of introducing ignition sources in these situations.	Workplace (Health, Safety and Welfare) Regulations 1992 (regulation 13) Control of Substances Hazardous to Health Regulations 1994 (COSHH)

List of agents, processes and work	What is the risk?
WORK INVOLVING THE RISK OF ACCIDENTS WHICH IT MAY BE ASSUMED CANNOT BE ATTENTION TO SAFETY OR LACK OF EXPERIENCE OR TRAINING *(continued)*	
Work involving a risk of structural collapse	There are a number of activities which may give rise to a ri of structural collapse, including new construction, refurbishment and alterations when structures may be eith deliberately or accidentally weakened. Demolition or dismantling is also a high-risk activity.
Work involving high-voltage electrical hazards	The risk is one of electric shock, burns or electrocution. There is no evidence that young workers face greater physi risks from electricity than other workers.

How to avoid the risk	Other legislation
ISED OR AVOIDED BY YOUNG WORKERS OWING TO THEIR INSUFFICIENT	
Employers should plan for all such work and it should be carried out under the control of a competent person. Young people should only do such work if properly trained or if they are under the supervision of a trained person.	Construction (Design and Management) Regulations 1994, Construction (Health, Safety and Welfare) Regulations 1996
As with adults, young people should not undertake any work involving electricity unless they have the necessary technical knowledge and/or experience to prevent danger or injury, or are under an appropriate level of supervision having regard to the nature of the work.	Electricity at Work Regulations 1989

List of agents, processes and work	What is the risk?
WORK IN WHICH THERE IS A RISK TO HEALTH FROM EXTREME COLD OR HEAT, OR FR	
Extreme cold or heat	Exposure to extreme heat carries risks for workers of all ag⟨ These include collapse due to heat exhaustion or potential⟩ fatal heat stroke. Protective clothing may prevent the body losing heat normally. Young workers control body temperature in the same way as older workers. Their response to work in hot conditions will depend on physical fitness, physique and past experience of hot conditions, which will be variable.

Exposure to extreme cold also carries risks for workers of a ages. These are principally hypothermia and local cold inju⟩ (frostnip/frostbite). People of all ages vary in their ability to tolerate cold conditions. |
| **Noise** | There is no evidence that young workers face greater risk o damaged hearing from exposure to noise than other worker |

How to avoid the risk	Other legislation
SE OR VIBRATION	
Any intended exposure to extreme heat must be carefully assessed and the risks can be minimised by measures such as introducing suitable work patterns, prior medical assessment of workers and proper supervision of the work.	Personal Protective Equipment at Work Regulations 1992, Workplace (Health, Safety and Welfare) Regulations 1992
Work in extreme cold must also be carefully assessed. The provision of appropriate protective clothing and control of work periods will help to minimise risk.	
Compliance with the Noise at Work Regulations should protect the hearing of young people. HSE has published guidance on ear protection, including the necessity of supervision, in noisy firms.	The Noise at Work Regulations 1989 apply to all workers exposed to loud noise where there is a risk to hearing.

List of agents, processes and work	What is the risk?
WORK IN WHICH THERE IS A RISK TO HEALTH FROM EXTREME COLD OR HEAT, OR F	
Hand-arm vibration	There is no evidence that young workers face a greater risk developing hand-arm vibration syndrome (vibration white finger) following exposure to hand-arm vibration than other workers. However, there is an increased risk in the onset o non-occupational Raynaud's disease during adolescence which can give similar symptoms to vibration white finger.
Whole-body vibration	Regular exposure to shocks, low-frequency whole-body vibration, eg driving or riding in off-road vehicles on uneve surfaces, or excessive movement may be associated with ba pain, and other spinal disorders. Younger workers may be greater risk of damage to the spine as the strength of the muscles is still developing and the bones do not fully matu until around the age of 25.

How to avoid the risk	Other legislation
ISE OR VIBRATION (*continued*)	
HSE has published guidance on hand-arm vibration. Employers will need to consider a programme to control the significant risks identified in the risk assessment including: identification of hazardous equipment/tasks; limiting exposure by reducing either the time and/or level; providing competent supervision; and health surveillance.	None specific
HSE has published guidance on whole-body vibration. Employers will need to consider a programme to control the significant risks identified in the risk assessment including identification of hazardous equipment/tasks; limiting exposure by reducing either the time and/or level; producing information and training on how to minimise the risk; and health surveillance.	None specific

APPENDIX 1 **Existing age-related restrictions**

Background

1   In general, restrictions on young people at work take the form of prohibitions, ie young people are not allowed to do the particular activity. Often the prohibitions only apply to specific activities in certain sectors of employment, for example, using lead glaze in pottery making. Sometimes they may be allowed to do the work if certain conditions (typically relating to training and/or supervision) are met. These restrictions also apply to pupils under the minimum school leaving age (MSLA) on work experience schemes.

2   Listed below are the *main employment and health and safety restrictions* relating to the work of young people (but not prohibitions that apply to workers of any age).

General legislation

3   *The Children and Young Persons Act 1933 (the Children and Young Persons (Scotland) Act 1937* in Scotland) limits employment to those aged 13 or above, although local authority bye-laws made under this legislation may permit children under this age to do light work on their family farm. *The Employment of Women, Young Persons and Children Act 1920* prohibits the employment of children under MSLA in any industrial undertaking. This includes construction, mines, quarries, manufacturing, transport, inland waterways and ships. Apart from this blanket prohibition of work in industrial undertakings, local authority bye-laws also contain restrictions on the types of work which children between the age of 13 and the MSLA may do. These bye-laws also restrict the number of hours which children may work, and generally require application to be made to the local education authority for an employment card to be issued before a child starts work. *The Children and Young Persons Act 1963* generally prohibits children under the MSLA from taking part in performances unless licensed to do so by the relevant local authority which takes account of the child's fitness and arrangements for their health, kind treatment and education.

Specific legislation

Explosives

4   *The Explosives Act 1875 (amended by the Explosives Act 1923)* and subsidiary legislation prohibits entry by people under 16 into any room where explosives are made, or where explosives (or their ingredients) are stored. (There are certain exceptions where a person under 16 is employed in a process which has been declared to be non-dangerous by an Order of the Secretary of State). People under 18 may not normally be employed in explosives buildings except in the presence and under the supervision of a person aged 21 or over. These requirements will be considered as part of the review of the Explosives Act 1875 which is currently underway and is planned for completion by the end of 1998.

5   The *Carriage of Explosives by Road Regulations 1996* prohibit any person under 18 from driving or attending an explosives vehicle, being employed as a driver or attendant, being responsible for the security of the explosives concerned, or entering the vehicle except under the supervision of someone aged more than 18. However, these prohibitions do not apply to the carriage of specified explosives with a slight risk, or to the carriage of limited quantities of certain other explosives.

Ionising radiation

6   Regulation 7 and Schedule 1 of the *Ionising Radiations Regulations 1985* set out a hierarchy of dose exposure limits, the highest being for an adult employee, followed by that for a trainee under 18 and then for 'any other person', eg a member of the public. Regulation 9 requires employers to classify employees likely to receive higher doses from radiation exposure but expressly prohibits a young person (under 18) from being designated as a 'classified person'. Following the recent adoption of a revised European Directive on protection against ionising radiations, these Regulations will undergo a programme of revision, and formal consultation is likely to commence in 1997. The general relationship between classification of persons and the work young people can do is unlikely to change, but the dose levels at which classification is required will be considerably lower.

Lead

7   There are various regulations that prohibit young people's work with lead. These are listed below. There are plans to consult on the possible removal of outdated prohibitions in 1997.

(a)   The *Paints and Colours Manufacture Regulations 1907* prohibit children (any young person under MSLA) and young people under 18 from handling dry lead carbonate, red lead or any colour incorporating these materials.

(b)   Regulation 10 of the *Lead Smelting and Manufacture Regulations 1911* prohibits the employment of any person under 16 in any lead process involving the smelting of materials containing lead; the manufacture of red or orange lead; and the manufacture of flaked litharge.

(c) The *Indiarubber Regulations 1922* prohibit any person under 16 and any female under 18 from weighing, manipulating or other treatment of any dry lead compound, including incorporation of dry lead compounds in Indiarubber.

(d) The *Electrical Accumulator Regulations 1925* prohibit the employment of any person under 18 in melting lead, or materials containing lead, casting, pasting, lead burning, or any other work involving the use, movement or handling of any lead oxide in the making of lead-acid batteries.

(e) The *Pottery (Health and Welfare) Special Regulations 1950* prohibit the employment of young people under 18 in specified processes and young people under 16 in other specific processes, particularly those involving the use or handling of materials with more than 5% lead content.

(f) Section 74 of the *Factories Act 1961* prohibits people under 18 from: work at furnaces where zinc or lead ores are reduced or treated; melting scrap lead or zinc; handling or treatment of ashes containing lead; desilvering lead; making solders or alloys containing more than 10% lead; making lead oxide, lead carbonate, lead sulphate, lead nitrate or lead silicate; mixing or pasting lead-mixtures for use in lead-acid batteries; and the cleaning of workrooms where any of the above processes are carried out.

(g) Section 131 of the *Factories Act 1961* prohibits people under 18 from painting any part of a building with lead paint.

(h) There are also prohibitions on the employment of people under 16 in particular processes involving lead in the *Yarn (Dyed by Lead Compounds) Heading Regulations 1907*; the *Vitreous Enamelling Regulations 1908*; and the *Tinning of Metal Hollow-Ware, Iron Drums and Harness Furniture Regulations 1909*.

Power presses

8   The *Power Presses Regulations 1965* prohibit any person under 18 from setting, adjusting or trying out the tools of a power press, or installing or adjusting safety devices on power presses in factories, unless undergoing training and under immediate supervision by a competent person. These Regulations are under review, as part of a general review of training and because of the review of the Provision and Use of Work Equipment Regulations 1992 (PUWER) which has similar requirements. The resulting proposals, which will necessitate the revocation of the 1965 Regulations, will be published in a Consultative Document in 1997.

Woodworking machines

9   Regulation 13(1) of the *Woodworking Machines Regulations 1974* prohibits any person from working at any woodworking machine in factories or on construction sites unless sufficiently trained and instructed or working under adequate supervision of a person who is knowledgeable and experienced. In addition, no person under 18 may operate, in factories or on construction

sites, certain woodworking machines including circular saws (not portable), planing machines used for surfacing (unless mechanically fed) and vertical spindle moulding machines (including high-speed routers) unless they have first successfully completed an approved course of training. Regulation 13 is due to be revoked in 1997 by the proposed Provision and Use of Work Equipment Regulations 1997 (PUWER). The requirements in the existing regulation 13 will be covered by regulation 9 of the new PUWER Regulations and a supporting ACOP. A Consultative Document outlining these proposals will be published in 1997.

10   Regulation 5 and Schedule 2 of the *Agriculture (Circular Saws) Regulations 1959* prohibit anyone from operating a circular saw on a farm or in other agricultural work, unless they are at least 16 and under the supervision of someone over 18 who has a knowledge of the working of the circular saw. These requirements are due to be reviewed in 1996/97.

Carriage of dangerous goods

11   Regulation 17 of the *Road Traffic (Carriage of Dangerous Substances in Road Tankers and Tank Containers) Regulations 1992* prohibits anyone not over 18 from being the supervisor of a road tanker or of a vehicle carrying a tank container when it is neither being driven nor parked on a safe place unless he or she is also the driver of the vehicle concerned; and Schedule 4 prohibits anyone not over 18 from being appointed to supervise the unloading of petrol from a road tanker at a petrol filling station.

12   Regulation 14 of the *Road Traffic (Carriage of Dangerous Substances in Packages etc.) Regulations 1992* prohibits anyone not over 18 from being the supervisor of a vehicle carrying a

dangerous substance when it is neither being driven nor parked in a safe place unless he or she is also the driver. These Regulations are to be revised. A Consultative Document proposing replacement of the above Regulations by the consolidated Carriage of Dangerous Goods by Road Regulations published in November 1995 provides an opportunity to identify the importance of age restriction.

Agriculture

13   The *Agriculture (Avoidance of Accidents to Children) Regulations 1958* prohibit children under 13 from riding on vehicles and machines including tractors, trailers etc. The associated ACOP *Preventing accidents to children in agriculture* offers practical advice on complying with health and safety legislation relating to children in the agricultural sector. This includes a list of machinery such as lift trucks and tractors carrying out certain operations that children are prohibited from doing until they reach MSLA. The Regulations and ACOP are due to be reviewed in 1996/97.

Lifting (docks and construction)

14   The following regulations are to be reviewed over the next three years, as part of the implementation of the amendment to the Use of Work Equipment Directive:

(a)   regulation 11 of the *Docks Regulations 1988*, prohibits any person under 18 from operating a powered lifting appliance in the course of dock operations, unless undergoing a suitable course of training under proper supervision of a competent person. Members of Her Majesty's Forces are exempt from this prohibition;

(b)   regulation 26(2) of the *Construction (Lifting Operations) Regulations 1961* prohibits any person under 18 from either giving signals to the operator of any mechanically-powered lifting appliance or to operate it unless under the direct supervision of a competent person.

Mines and quarries

15   Age limits in mines and quarries legislation are being considered in the Mines and Quarries legislative review programme over the next five to six years.

16   Section 42(1) of the *Mines and Quarries Act 1954* specifies an age limit of 22 and above for those in charge of winding and rope haulage equipment, when people are transported; section 43(2) specifies an age limit of 18 and above for those in charge of rope haulage when people are not carried; and section 44 specifies an age limit of 18 and above for those in charge of conveyors at work faces. These sections apply only to mines and will be reviewed in the context of proposals on underground transport in mines and consultation is due in 1997. This review will also include:

(a)   regulation 21 of the *Coal and Other Mines (Sidings) Regulations 1956* which prohibits people under 18 from being employed as locomotive drivers or those under 16 as shunters;

(b)   regulation 17 of the *Coal and Other Mines (Locomotives) Regulations 1956* which prohibits any person under 21 (under 18 in a mine of shale) to operate a locomotive hauling people.

17   A Consultative Document for the Quarries Consolidation Package reviewing the following legislation (among others) is planned to be published in March 1997:

(a)   regulation 36 of the *Quarries (General) Regulations 1956* prohibits the employment of any person under 18 in a quarry for the purpose of driving a locomotive and the employment of any person under 16 as a shunter;

(b)   regulation 13(1) of the *Quarries (Ropeways and Vehicles) Regulations 1958* prohibits the employment of any person under 21 to drive a haulage vehicle, or operate any mechanical apparatus used for moving any conveyance or vehicle;

(c)   regulation 9 of the *Quarry Vehicles Regulations 1970* states that no person under 17 may drive a quarry vehicle, unless under supervision for training purposes;

(d)   regulation 4 of the *Quarries (Explosives) Regulations 1988* states that a manager of a quarry must have reached 21. Regulation 7 prohibits the appointment of a shotfirer under 21.

18   Work will start to review the following legislation in 1997/98:

(a)   regulation 3 of the *Stratified Ironstone, Shale and Fireclay Mines (Explosives Regulations) 1956* which prohibits the appointment of any person as a shotfirer unless they have reached 21;

(b)   regulation 6 of the *Miscellaneous (Mines Explosives) Regulations 1959* which prohibits the appointment of any person under 21 as a shotfirer;

(c) regulation 4(4) of the *Coal and Other Safety Lamp Mines (Explosives) Regulations 1993*, which prohibits the appointment of any person as a shotfirer unless they are at least 21 and hold HSE-approved qualifications or are otherwise suitably qualified.

Shipbuilding

19 Regulation 80(1) of the *Shipbuilding and Ship-repairing Regulations 1960*, states that no young person under 16 shall, until he has been employed in a shipyard for at least six months, be employed where he is liable to fall more than 6 feet 6 inches, or into water in which there is a risk of drowning. Regulation 80(2) requires such young people to be under the charge of an experienced worker. Under the Health and Safety Commission's Review of Regulation, these Regulations were recommended for revocation when new generic regulations are in place. A Consultative Document reviewing the remaining parts of ship building legislation, including this prohibition, will be issued in 1998.

APPENDIX 2   **References and further reading**

HSE Approved Codes of Practice (ACOPs)

Control of lead at work Approved Code of Practice COP2 (rev) HSE Books 1985
ISBN 0 7176 1046 2

General COSHH ACOP (Control of substances hazardous to health) and Carcinogens ACOP (Control of carcinogenic substances) and Biological agents ACOP (Control of biological agents). Control of Substances Hazardous to Health Regulations 1994 Approved Codes of Practice L5 HSE Books 1995
ISBN 0 7176 0819 0

Management of health and safety at work. Management of Health and Safety at Work Regulations 1992 Approved Code of Practice L21 HSE Books 1992 ISBN 0 7176 0412 8

The protection of persons against ionising radiation arising from any work activity. The Ionising Radiations Regulations 1985 Approved Code of Practice Parts 1 & 2 L58 HSE Books 1985
ISBN 0 7176 0508 6

HSE guidance

Hand-arm vibration HS(G)88 HSE Books 1994
ISBN 0 7176 0743 7

Preventing asthma at work: How to control respiratory sensitisers L55 HSE Books 1994
ISBN 0 7176 0661 9

In the driving seat: Advice to employers on reducing back pain in drivers and machinery operators Free leaflet IND(G)242L HSE Books 1997 (Available in priced packs for multiple copies on ISBN 0 7176 1314 3 at £5.00 per pack)

Preventing dermatitis at work: Advice for employers and employees Free leaflet IND(G)233(L) HSE Books 1996 (Available in priced packs for multiple copies on ISBN 0 7176 1246 5 at £5.00 per pack)

Ear protection in noisy firms - Employers' duties explained Free leaflet IND(G)200(L) HSE Books 1995 (Available in priced packs for multiple copies on ISBN 0 7176 0924 3 at £5.00 per pack)

Keep your top on: Health risks from working in the sun Free leaflet IND(G)147(L) HSE Books 1993 (Available in priced packs for multiple copies on ISBN 0 7176 0988 X at £5.00 per pack)

Other guidance

IRPA guidelines on protection against non-ionising radiation Pergamon Press 1991 ISBN 0 08 036097 1

Board statement on restrictions on human exposure to static and time varying electromagnetic fields and radiation. Documents of the NRPB Vol. 4 No 5 Didcot 1993 ISBN 0 85951 366 1

Board statement on effects of ultraviolet radiation on human health and health effects from ultraviolet radiation. Documents of the NRPB Vol. 6 No 2 1995 ISBN 0 85951 387 4

Department for Education and Employment: Education at work: A guide for employers. Work experience and related activities for pupils under 16 1988 Available from DfEE Publications Centre, PO Box 6927, London E3 7NZ Tel: 0171 510 0150 Fax: 0171 510 0196

Department for Education and Employment: Education at work: A guide for schools.
Work experience and related activities for pupils under 16 1988 Available from DfEE Publications Centre, PO Box 6927, London E3 7NZ Tel: 0171 510 0150 Fax: 0171 510 0196

For details of how to obtain HSE free and priced publications, see inside back cover.

YOUNG PEOPLE AT WORK *Questionnaire*

To help us assess this publication, will you please complete this questionnaire (tick box or ring number as appropriate) and return it to the address overleaf. Postage is free.

Name: ....

Company/organisation: ....

Address: ....

....

....

....

Post code: ....

Nature of business:

Manufacturing

        Main activity: ....

Retailing

Transport

Warehousing

Professional services

Local/National government

Trade Association

Employees Association

Did you find the guidance: *Very useful*   *Not useful*
                                         1   2   3   4

Was the information presented: *Well*   *Poorly*
                                         1   2   3   4

Was the layout: *Clear*   *Difficult to follow*
                                       1   2   3   4

Did you find the guidance clear, concise and easy to follow?   Yes ☐   No ☐

Did the publication contain the information you expected?   Yes ☐   No ☐

If not, what other information would you have expected?

....

....

....

Did you feel that the publication represents: *Very good value*   *Poor value for money*
                                                1   2   3   4

Have you taken any action or changed any procedures as a result of reading this publication?   Yes ☐   No ☐
If so, what?

....

....

Have you any other comments about this publication?

....

....

....

Thank you for taking the time to answer these questions

THIRD FOLD

BUSINESS REPLY SERVICE
Licence No. LV 5189

FIRST FOLD

SECOND FOLD

Health and Safety Executive
Room 303
Daniel House
Stanley Precinct
Bootle
Merseyside L20 7HE

FOURTH FOLD

Tuck A into B to form envelope
Please do not staple or glue